Design a Habitat

Description

After reading a picture book about a boy who is begging his mom for a pet iguana, students explore the phenomenon of different kinds of animals living in different places on Earth. They learn about the needs of living things and the diverse habitats that meet those needs. Engineering design comes into play when students apply their knowledge about the needs of animals by designing and building a model habitat for an imaginary pet of their own.

Alignment With the *Next Generation Science Standards*

Performance Expectations

K-LS1-1: Use observations to describe patterns of what plants and animals (including humans) need to survive.

K-2-ETS1-2: Develop a simple sketch, drawing, or physical model to illustrate how the shape of an object helps it function as needed to solve a given problem.

Science and Engineering Practices	Disciplinary Core Ideas	Crosscutting Concepts
Developing and Using Models Develop a simple model based on evidence to represent a proposed object or tool. **Engaging in Argument From Evidence** Construct an argument with evidence to support a claim.	**LS1.C: Organization for Matter and Energy Flow in Organisms** All animals need food in order to live and grow. They obtain their food from plants or from other animals. Plants need water and light to live and grow. **ETS1.B: Developing Possible Solutions** Designs can be conveyed through sketches, drawings, or physical models. These representations are useful in communicating ideas for a problem's solutions to other people.	**Patterns** Patterns in the natural and human-designed world can be observed, used to describe phenomena, and used as evidence.

Note: The activities in this lesson will help students move toward the performance expectations listed, which is the goal after multiple activities. However, the activities will not by themselves be sufficient to reach the performance expectations.

Featured Picture Books

TITLE: *I Wanna Iguana*
AUTHOR: **Karen Kaufman Orloff**
ILLUSTRATOR: **David Catrow**
PUBLISHER: **Putnam**
YEAR: **2004**
GENRE: **Story**
SUMMARY: *Alex and his mother write notes back and forth in which Alex tries to persuade her to let him have a baby iguana for a pet.*

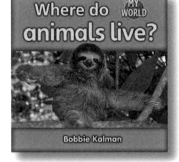

TITLE: *Where Do Animals Live?*
AUTHOR: **Bobbie Kalman**
PUBLISHER: **Crabtree**
YEAR: **2010**
GENRE: **Non-Narrative Information**
SUMMARY: *Simple text and photographs describe the basic needs of living things and how different habitats meet the needs of different animals.*

Time Needed

This lesson will take several class periods. Suggested scheduling is as follows:

Session 1: Engage with *I Wanna Iguana* Read-Aloud and **Explore** with Observing Iguanas

Session 2: Explain with *Where Do Animals Live?* Read-Aloud and Animal Habitat Sort

Session 3: Elaborate with Design a Habitat Challenge and Animal Enrichment

Session 4: Evaluate with *I Wanna Iguana* Rereading and Write a Letter

Materials

- Measuring tape
- World map or globe

For Animal Habitat Sort (per group of 2–3 students)

- Habitat Cards
- Plastic sandwich bag containing 1 animal figurine from each of the following 5 Safari Ltd TOOB sets:
  - 1 Arctic TOOB (polar habitat)
  - 1 Desert TOOB (desert habitat)
  - 1 Ocean TOOB (ocean habitat)
  - 1 Rainforest TOOB (rainforest habitat)
  - 1 Nature TOOB (grassland habitat)

TOOB figurines can be purchased at
Amazon.com and *Michaels.com*.

National Science Teaching Association

Note: You will need to omit or move some of the TOOB figurines to fit the habitats identified in this lesson (see Table 15.1 on the next page). You will have enough animal figurines for up to 9 groups of 2–3 students.

For Design a Habitat Challenge (per student)

- Lunch-sized paper bag
- Animal figurines from Animal Habitat Sort
- Shoe box

Student Pages

- Habitat Cards
- Design a Habitat Challenge
- Animal Fact Card
- Write a Letter
- STEM Everywhere

Background for Teachers

Living things need food, water, and air to survive. They also need space to live and, in many cases, shelter from the elements. Those are considered basic needs. Although living things have the same basic needs in common, they meet those needs in diverse ways. For example, animals fulfill their need for food by eating plants or other animals. Plants, however, make their own food using air, water, and sunlight through the process of *photosynthesis*. Plants obtain water and air through their roots and leaves. Animals have many different ways of meeting their needs for water and air. For example, some animals, such as fish, breathe air that is dissolved in water through their gills. Other animals, such as birds and mammals, breathe air through their lungs. Some desert animals, such as jackrabbits, can obtain water by eating plants that store water; some animals, such as deer, drink water from puddles, streams, and lakes. The way an animal meets its needs depends on the habitat in which it lives.

Living things can only live in places that can fulfill their basic needs. A *habitat* is the immediate environment in which a living thing fulfills its basic needs. It can be as large as a forest or as small as a tide pool or rotting log. Different animals are suited for different habitats. This lesson features five distinct habitats—polar, desert, ocean, rainforest, and grassland—but there are many more.

When an animal lives in a zoo, an artificial habitat must be designed to meet its needs. Designers of zoo habitats must research the animal's natural habitat and replicate it as authentically as possible given the constraints of the exhibit space at the zoo. The designer must not only consider the basic needs of food, water, and air but also research the animal's behaviors and create *animal enrichment* activities that enhance their well-being. Enrichment can include a place for an animal to climb, a challenge to capture its food, or even a toy to play with. Enrichment goes beyond the basic physical needs of animals and addresses their psychological needs. Many zoos have information on their websites about the enrichment they provide for their animals.

Table 15.1. TOOB Habitats Chart

Polar (sold as Arctic TOOB)	Desert	Ocean	Rainforest	Grassland (sold as Nature TOOB)
(Remove igloo and humans.) Arctic fox Arctic rabbit Beluga whale Caribou Harp seal Husky Killer whale Penguin* Polar bear Walrus *Move here from Ocean TOOB.	*(Remove human and cactus.)* Armadillo Bobcat Coyote Desert bighorn ram Horned lizard Mountain lion Rattlesnake Road runner Scorpion	Dolphin Beluga whale Eagle ray Hammerhead shark Humpback whale Killer whale Moray eel Octopus Sea lion Sea turtle Sperm whale Starfish Tiger shark	*(Remove human.)* Anteater Caiman Emerald tree boa Iguana Jaguar Poison dart frog Red-and-blue macaw Red-eyed tree frog Spider monkey Tapir Toco toucan	Bald eagle Beaver Black bear Buffalo Cardinal Doe Fox Gray wolf Moose Mountain lion Prairie dog* Rabbit Raccoon *Move here from Desert TOOB.

In this lesson, students learn about the needs of living things through a nonfiction read-aloud. They learn that animals and plants acquire food differently—plants make food with water, light, and air, whereas animals eat plants or other animals. The crosscutting concept (CCC) of patterns is addressed as students recognize patterns of where different animals live. Animals are suited to live in those habitats that meet their basic needs. Students then apply their knowledge to a design challenge where they design a habitat to meet the needs of a certain animal, making a physical model of the habitat using a shoe box and art supplies, which applies the science and engineering practice (SEP) of developing and using models. Students engage in argument from evidence (another SEP) as they explain how the habitat and enrichment activities in their models meet the animal's basic needs.

Learning Progressions

Below are the DCI grade band endpoints for grades K–2 and 3–5. These are provided to show how student understanding of the DCIs in this lesson will progress in future grade levels.

DCIs	Grades K–2	Grades 3–5
LS1.C: Organization for Matter and Energy Flow in Organisms	• All animals need food in order to live and grow. They obtain their food from plants or from other animals. Plants need water and light to live and grow.	• Food provides animals with the materials they need for body repair and growth and the energy they need to maintain body warmth and for motion. • Plants acquire their material for growth chiefly from air and water.
ETS1.B: Developing Possible Solutions	• Designs can be conveyed through sketches, drawings, or physical models. These representations are useful in communicating ideas for a problem's solutions to other people.	• At whatever stage, communicating with peers about proposed solutions is an important part of the design process, and shared ideas can lead to improved designs.

Source: Willard, T., ed. 2015. *The NSTA quick-reference guide to the* NGSS: *Elementary school.* Arlington, VA: NSTA Press.

engage

I Wanna Iguana Read-Aloud

Connecting to the Common Core
Reading: Literature
KEY IDEAS AND DETAILS: K.1

Inferring

Show students the cover of *I Wanna Iguana* and introduce the author and illustrator. *Ask*

? What do you think this book might be about? (Answers will vary.)

? What is an iguana? (Answers will vary.)

? Do you know anyone who has a pet iguana? (Answers will vary.)

Then, read the book aloud.

Questioning

After reading, share the back-cover information about author Karen Kaufman Orloff and how she was inspired to write this book after her son talked her into buying him a pet iguana. *Ask*

? How did Alex persuade his mom to let him have a pet iguana? (He wrote her letters and gave reasons the iguana would be a good pet to have.)

? Would you want a pet iguana? (Answers will vary.)

? What do you think you might need to take good care of an iguana? (Answers will vary.)

explore

Observing Iguanas

Connecting to the Common Core
Reading: Informational Text
Key Ideas and Details: K.1

Tell students that before you get any kind of pet, it is important to research the animal's needs. This means finding out what it needs to stay alive. Tell students that zoos research their animals' needs in order to keep them alive and healthy in captivity. Show students the *Growing Up Wild* episode featuring Shrek, a green iguana who lives at the Australia Zoo, and have them listen to Robert Irwin for information on what green iguanas need to stay alive and healthy. The episode is available at online (see "Websites" section).

Questioning

After the video, *ask*

? What do green iguanas eat? (vegetables and flowers; some insects when young but mostly vegetation)

? What are green iguanas good at doing? (climbing trees and swimming)

? Where did Robert Irwin say green iguanas can be found? (Florida)

? Why is that a problem? (They are escaped pets and don't belong there.)

? So where *do* green iguanas belong? (Answers will vary, and students will find out from the research that follows.)

? What would Alex need to provide for his baby green iguana to stay alive and healthy? (water to drink; food such as leaves, flowers, and fruit; space to climb; space to swim, etc.)

Explain that water, food, air, and space/shelter are basic needs of all animals. *Ask*

? How much space do you think a baby green iguana would need? (It needs a small amount of space at first, but green iguanas can grow to be over 6 feet long!)

Explain that animals can only stay alive and healthy in a place that can meet their basic needs.

Next, tell students that you can find out more about green iguanas, including where they belong in the wild, from National Geographic's Green Iguana web page (see "Websites" section). Show students the web page's green iguana photo gallery and have them make observations as you flip through the 20 or more slides in the gallery.

Turn and Talk

As you are showing the photos, have students turn to a partner and share what they observe. Then have students share with the class what they observed about green iguanas from the photos. They should be able to notice the following:

• Green iguanas are green, but also blue, brown, and red.

• They have scaly skin.

• They have sharp claws.

• They have spines along their backs.

• They eat vegetation such as flowers.

• They can swim.

• They drink water.

• They live in trees/jungles.

Then scroll up the page and paraphrase the following facts about the green iguana:

• Green, or common, iguanas are among the largest lizards in the Americas, averaging around 6.5 feet long and weighing about 11 pounds. (Show students how long 6.5 feet is using a measuring tape.)

• They are also among the most popular reptile pets in the United States, despite being quite difficult to care for properly.

• The green iguana's extensive range comprises the rain forests of northern Mexico, Central

America, the Caribbean Islands, and southern Brazil. (Show the green iguana's range on a map or globe.)

- Primarily herbivores (plant eaters), iguanas are active during the day, feeding on leaves, flowers, and fruit. They generally live near water and are excellent swimmers.

explain

Where Do Animals Live? Read-Aloud

Connecting to the Common Core
Reading: Informational Text
KEY IDEAS AND DETAILS: K.1

OBSERVING ANIMAL FIGURINES

Determining Importance

Show students the cover of *Where Do Animals Live?* and introduce the author, Bobbie Kalman. Tell students that this book will help them understand more about the basic needs of iguanas and other animals. Have students signal (raise their hands) when they hear about basic needs as you read the book aloud. Students should signal when you get to page 6. Then, *ask*

? What do animals need to survive? (air, food, and water, as well as shelter or space, which is not mentioned in the book)

Tell students that plants also have basic needs. Like animals, plants need food to live and grow, but plants do not eat food—they make it! Plants make food using sunlight, air, and water. *Ask*

? What is the difference between what plants need and what animals need? (Animals eat their food; plants make their own food.)

Continue reading through page 11. Then, explain that the iguana pictured is different from the green iguana featured in *I Wanna Iguana*. This iguana lives in the desert and eats cacti. There is

another kind of iguana called a *marine iguana* that lives near the ocean and spends a lot of its time underwater. These three types of iguanas live in different places, or habitats, to meet their needs.

Continue reading pages 11–12, and explain that these cold habitats are also called *polar habitats*.

Questioning

Read the rest of the book aloud, noting the different animals that live in each habitat. After reading, check for understanding. *Ask*

? What is a habitat? (a place where certain types of animals live)

? What kinds of habitats were described in the book? (forest, desert, mountain, grassland, polar, wetland, and ocean)

Explain that there are many other kinds of habitats, but for the next activity, you will focus on the polar, desert, ocean, rainforest, and grassland habitats.

Animal Habitat Sort

Give each group of two to three students a set of five animal figurines—one from each of the five habitats (see Table 15.1). Allow students time to make some observations of their five figurines.

ANIMAL HABITAT SORT

Then, *ask*

? What do all of your figurines have in common? (They are all animals.)

? How are they different? (They are different kinds of animals, and they are different colors and shapes. Some have legs, some have wings, some have fins, etc.)

? According to the book we just read, what do they all need to survive? (air, food, and water)

? Do you think all of these animals live in the same place in the wild? (no)

? Do you think they all eat the same kind of food? (no)

> **CCC: Patterns**
> Patterns in the natural world can be observed, used to describe phenomena, and used as evidence.

Connecting to the Common Core
Reading: Informational Text
CRAFT AND STRUCTURE: 1.5

Using Features of Nonfiction

Remind students that all animals have the same basic needs: water, air, food, and shelter/space. However, different animals need different kinds of food, and animals get water in different ways. Some animals do best in very cold places, whereas others are healthiest in warm places. Some animals' needs are met underwater, and other animals' needs are met in very dry places. Give each group a set of the five Habitat Cards. Choose one of the habitats from the cards (polar, desert, ocean, rainforest, and grassland), and model how to use the table of contents to find the section of the book that discusses that habitat. Reread that section of the book. *Ask*

? Does anyone have a figurine of a type of animal that might live in that habitat? (Answers will vary.)

? What makes you think that animal might live there? (Answers will vary.)

Have students place the animal on the corresponding Habitat Card. Repeat the sorting procedure with the other Habitat Cards. Students should try to match one animal to each habitat. Keep in mind that the main goal of this activity is for students to learn that different animals are suited for different habitats. It is not essential that they get the "right" answer for each animal, because they are relying primarily on their own schema to sort the animals (which will vary from student to student). However, the correct answers are shown in Table 15.2.

After students have sorted their animals into the different habitats, each group can trade animals with another group and sort those animals.

Table 15.2. Answer Key for Animal Habitat Sort

Polar	Desert	Ocean	Rainforest	Grassland
Arctic fox Arctic rabbit Beluga whale* Caribou Harp seal Husky Killer whale* Penguin Polar bear Walrus *Ocean is also an acceptable answer.	Armadillo Bobcat* Coyote* Desert bighorn ram Horned lizard Mountain lion* Rattlesnake* Road runner Scorpion *Grassland is also an acceptable answer.	Dolphin Eagle ray Hammerhead shark Humpback whale Moray eel Octopus Sea lion Sea turtle Sperm whale Starfish Tiger shark	Anteater Caiman Emerald tree boa Iguana Jaguar Poison dart frog Red-and-blue macaw Red-eyed tree frog Spider monkey Tapir Toco toucan	Bald eagle Beaver Black bear Buffalo Cardinal Doe Fox Gray wolf Moose Mountain lion* Prairie dog* Rabbit* Raccoon *Desert is also an acceptable answer.

elaborate

Design a Habitat Challenge

Tell students that, as the character Alex did in *I Wanna Iguana,* they are going to try to persuade their parents to let them have a pet! This won't be just any pet, however—it will be one of the animals from the set of figurines they used. By designing a model of a habitat for the animal (using a shoe box and supplies from home), they will prove to their parents that they could meet all of the animal's needs. They will also be writing a letter to their parents to persuade them. Students should realize that most of the figurines are not of animals that would actually be kept as pets. In fact, many of these animals would be somewhat ridiculous (and possibly even dangerous!) to have as pets. Remind students that wild animals should never be kept as pets. Explain that because the activity is just pretend, they can feel free to design a habitat that is huge and elaborate. The only limit is their imagination!

Animal Enrichment

Explain that although most of the animals from the figurine sets would not be appropriate pets for people to keep in their homes, some of them are kept in zoos. Tell students that zoos must not only make sure that an animal's basic needs (food, water, air, and shelter/space) are met in order to keep it alive, but also provide things to keep the animal healthy and happy. Providing for needs beyond basic ones is called *animal enrichment.* Show students some examples of animal enrichment from zoos around the country (see "Recommended Websites for Animal Habitat Enrichment" section). Tell students that they will need to design at least one enrichment activity when they create their habitats.

> **SEP: Developing and Using Models**
> Develop a model based on evidence to represent a proposed object or tool.

POLAR HABITAT MODELS

to decide whether the students will be expected to return the figurines to you after the assignment is turned in and displayed. It is best to let them know in advance!

evaluate

I Wanna Iguana Rereading

Connecting to the Common Core
Reading: Literature
KEY IDEAS AND DETAILS: K.1

Rereading

Ask students to recall how the character Alex in *I Wanna Iguana* wrote a series of persuasive letters to his mom. Tell students that they will be writing similar letters to a family member to persuade them to let them keep the animals for which they built the model habitats. Explain that although it would be ridiculous and possibly even dangerous to keep their animal as a pet, thinking about what it would be like to have one is fun and a good way to show what they know about that animal and its needs. Reread some of the letters from *I Wanna Iguana*, including pages 24–25, showing the iguana on the diving board. Ask students to listen for the reasons or arguments that Alex gives to persuade his mom to let him get an iguana. *Ask*

? How did Alex convince his mom that he could take care of the iguana's basic needs? (He told her that he would feed him every day, make sure the iguana had enough water, and clean the iguana's cage when it got messy.)

? Why do you think Alex's mom finally gave in? (He was persistent, he gave a lot of reasons for why he should have the iguana, he convinced her that he could take care of the iguana's basic needs, etc.)

Next, place all the figurines in a lunch-sized paper bag. Have students each pull an animal out of the bag. (The more outlandish the "pets" are, the more fun the activity.) Explain that the animal each student randomly selects is the animal for which he or she will be designing a "habitat in a box."

Give each student a copy of the Design a Habitat Challenge student page and the Animal Fact Card student page. Have them write their name and the name of the animal on the Animal Fact Card, and then sketch the animal in the box at the bottom (students may want to trace the outline of the figurine). Explain that they will be doing research at home with an adult helper to find out more about the animal's needs and its habitat. You may want to send home a list of recommended websites for students to use with their family for research (see "Recommended Websites for Animal Research" section). Review the directions together. Then, send the animal figurine and the assignment home to be completed as homework. Students will need to cut out and attach the completed Animal Fact Card to a shoe box and also place the animal in the habitat model for display in the classroom. Review the directions on the student page together.

Note: The name of the animal is printed on each figurine. You may need to help students find the name because it is in very small print. You need

Write a Letter

**Writing**

Now, students can write a persuasive letter asking their parents or guardians to let them keep the animals in the habitats they designed. Give each student a copy of the Write a Letter student page. In their letters, they should explain how they will meet the animal's needs and why they should be able to keep it.

> **SEP: Engaging in Argument From Evidence**
> Construct an argument with evidence to support a claim.

STEM Everywhere

Give students the STEM Everywhere student page as a way to involve their families and extend their learning. They can do the activity with an adult helper and share their results with the class. If students do not have access to the internet at home, you may choose to show the video at school.

Opportunities for Differentiated Instruction

This box lists questions and challenges related to the lesson that students may select to research, investigate, or innovate. Students may also use the questions as examples to help them generate their own questions. These questions can help you move your students from the teacher-directed investigation to engaging in the science and engineering practices in a more student-directed format.

Extra Support

For students who are struggling to meet the lesson objectives, provide a question and guide them in the process of collecting research or helping them design procedures or solutions.

Extensions

For students with high interest or who have already met the lesson objectives, have them choose a question (or pose their own question), conduct their own research, and design their own procedures or solutions.

After selecting one of the questions in this box or formulating their own questions, students can individually or collaboratively make predictions, design investigations or surveys to test their predictions, collect evidence, devise explanations, design solutions, or examine related resources. They can communicate their findings through a science notebook, at a poster session or gallery walk, or by producing a media project.

Research

Have students brainstorm researchable questions:

? Who designs zoo habitats?

Continued

Opportunities for Differentiated Instruction (continued)

? What does your local zoo do for animal enrichment?

? What animals would make good classroom pets? What would they need to be happy and healthy?

Investigate

Have students brainstorm testable questions to be solved through science or math:

? Survey your friends and family: "Would you rather live in a polar, desert, ocean, rainforest, or grassland habitat?" Graph the results, and then analyze your graph. What can you conclude?

? Survey your friends and family: "What kinds of pets do you have at home?" Graph the results, and then analyze your graph. What can you conclude?

? Survey your friends and family: "If you could keep any animal as a pet, which animal would you choose?" Graph the results, and then analyze your graph. What can you conclude?

Innovate

Have students brainstorm problems to be solved through engineering:

? Can you design an enrichment activity for a favorite zoo animal? (Check out the videos in the "Recommended Websites for Animal Habitat Enrichment" section.)

? Can you design a model habitat for an animal at your local zoo?

? Can you design an enrichment toy or activity for your family or classroom pet?

Websites

 "Growing Up Wild: Green Iguana" Video
*www.youtube.com/
watch?v=02Qpg6t_HUM*

 National Geographic Green Iguana
*www.nationalgeographic.com/
animals/reptiles/g/green-iguana*

Recommended Websites for Animal Habitat Enrichment

 Phoenix Zoo Behavioral Enrichment
*www.phoenixzoo.org/explore/
enrichment-care*

 Saint Louis Zoo Animal Enrichment (includes videos)
*www.stlzoo.org/animals/
enrichmenttraining/animalenrichment*

Recommended Websites for Animal Research

 National Geographic Kids
*http://kids.nationalgeographic.com/
animals*

 San Diego Zoo Kids
https://kids.sandiegozoo.org/animals

 Wild Kratts Creaturepedia
*https://pbskids.org/wildkratts/
creaturepedia*

National Science Teaching Association

More Books to Read

Jenkins, S., and R. Page. 2016. *I see a kookaburra.* New York: HMH Books for Young Readers.
Summary: Jenkins's trademark paper-collage artwork depicts six different habitats and the animals that live in each.

Na, I. S. 2015. *Welcome home bear: A book of animal habitats.* New York: Knopf Books for Young Readers.
Summary: Bear begins to look for a new place to live. He visits several habitats and discovers that his own habitat is the perfect place for him to live after all.

Nun, D. 2012. *Why living things need ... Food.* Chicago: Heinemann.
Summary: From the *Why Living Things Need ...* series, this book uses simple text and photographs to explain that living things need food; plants make their own food using water, air, and sunlight; and animals eat plants or other animals. Other titles in this series include *Air, Homes, Light,* and *Water.*

Pattison, D. 2014. *I want a dog: My opinion essay.* Little Rock, AR: Mims House.
Summary: Dennis writes an opinion essay for his teacher. But will his essay persuade his parents to get the dog of his dreams? The book includes information on dog breeds and responsible dog ownership.

Pattison, D. 2015. *I want a cat: My opinion essay.* Little Rock, AR: Mims House.
Summary: Mellie writes an opinion essay for her teacher. But will her essay persuade her parents to get the cat of her dreams? The book includes information on cat breeds and responsible cat ownership.

Seuss, Dr. 2015. *What pet should I get?* New York: Random House.
Summary: This Dr. Seuss book follows the signature style of illustration and rhyme as a brother and sister go to a pet store and can't decide which pet to buy. The "Editor's Note" at the end of the book contains information on Dr. Seuss (Theodor Geisel) and his love for animals (with photos of him and some of his pets), his writing process, and how the manuscript was discovered.

Habitat Cards

Directions:
Cut out the cards and match the animal figurines to the correct habitat.

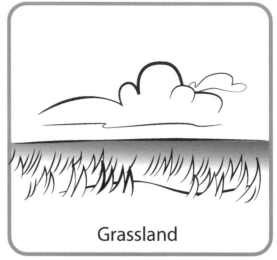
Grassland

Desert

Rainforest

Polar

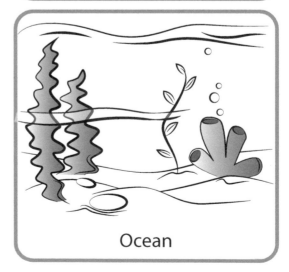
Ocean

National Science Teaching Association

Name: _____

Design a Habitat Challenge

Challenge: Design and build a habitat model for your animal! Work with an adult helper to do the following:

1. Find out about your animal's needs.

2. Find out what your animal's natural habitat looks like.

3. Fill out the Animal Fact Card.

4. Design and build your model using a shoe box and other materials. Your model should include the figurine.

5. Cut out the Animal Fact Card and attach it to your shoe box.

Check (✓) that your habitat model meets your animal's needs:

☐ **Food to eat**

☐ **Water to drink**

☐ **Air to breathe**

☐ **Activity or toy for enrichment**

Name: _____

Animal Fact Card

Animal:
_____

Eats:
_____

Drinks:
_____

Lives:
_____

National Science Teaching Association

Write a Letter

Dear _____ ,

I want a _____

_____

_____

_____

_____

_____

_____

From, _____

Name: _____

STEM Everywhere

Dear Families,

At school, we have been learning that **animals live in habitats that meet their basic needs.** To find out more, ask your learner the following questions and discuss their answers:

- What did you learn?
- What was your favorite part of the lesson?
- What are you still wondering?

 At home, you can create a "mixed-up" animal and design a habitat for it. Scan the QR code, search YouTube for "Crazy Mixed Up Animal Game," or go to *www.youtube.com/watch?v=rsqMuOpWKuc.*

1. Watch the video mentioned above and then create a new "mixed-up" animal.

2. Give your new animal a fun name like the animals in the video have.

3. Design a habitat with everything the animal would need to meet its basic needs.

4. In the box below, draw and label your "mixed-up" animal in its habitat.

_____

"Mixed-Up" Animal Name

National Science Teaching Association